FLY·FISHING LOGBOOK

f-stop Fitzgerald

A BULFINCH PRESS BOOK

LITTLE, BROWN AND COMPANY

BOSTON   NEW YORK   TORONTO   LONDON

THIS BOOK IS DEDICATED TO
GRANDPA AND DAD FOR TEACHING ME
AND TO GENNI AND WESTON FOR LEARNING

Cover photo: Gold and Black
Endpapers photo: Detail from Ed Hewitt's fly box
Title page photo: Red Quill, dry and wet, by Ed Hewitt
Photograph of Emily Rutherfoord Royall:
Courtesy of the Williams family archives, photographer unknown

A Balliett & Fitzgerald Book

First Edition

ISBN O-8212-2163-9

Design by Elizabeth H. Granatelli

Bulfinch Press is an imprint and trademark of
Little, Brown and Company (Inc.)

Published simultaneously in Canada by
Little, Brown & Company (Canada) Limited

PRINTED IN HONG KONG

TABLE OF CONTENTS

GRANDPA'S
LITTLE BLACK BOOK

by *f*-stop Fitzgerald

In the days before there were thermocline indicators, depth finders, color Sea-lectors and LORAN navigational devices, the smart angler kept a logbook in which was written every detail of his or her sport, from tools to tides, catch to conditions. As the challenge of angling for gamefish often benefits from good record-keeping, even today there's no better way to keep track of what worked and what didn't. So if, as the great fishing writer Sparse Grey Hackle reportedly said, "The finest fishing often takes place not on water, but in print," then you hold in your hands a book that will allow for the opportunity to create your own fine fishing.

My introduction to the practice of keeping a fishing logbook occurred when I met my wife's grandparents, Clarence Stewart Alexander Williams and his fiercely proud southern wife Emily Rutherfoord Royall. Unfortunately Grandpa Williams passed away before I could get to know him well; but he left behind a mystery that I am still trying to unravel.

Emily and Clarence Williams had done pretty well in life. They had a large happy family with children, grandchildren and great-grandchildren, and they had been successful in business. By the time I met them, they were spending their summers on Wolf Island, up on the Saint Lawrence River. They had a beautiful cabin cruiser, with a hull of brilliant red cherrywood which seemed to glow. A huge Mercury outboard hung off the back. Their only gear consisted of medium-action bait casting rigs; nothing fancy, and no electronics.

But Grandpa had one secret—a little, black book in which every day he noted every detail about every place and every fish.

Grandpa had worked hard enough to now spend every navigable day of each summer out on the water of the Saint Lawrence—big water, with big fish. Granny was genteel enough to actually want to spend part of these days with her husband, so she would go out with Grandpa every morning, sometimes fishing and always sharing her husband's angling joy.

One rough day they were out in the channel, without much going on. But this day, Granny decided to try her hand at it, regardless of the likelihood of getting a bite. She picked out one of the old-fashioned wooden casting plugs. Grandpa reputedly told her it was the wrong color, and that no self-respecting fish in the whole river would even look at it, let alone strike it. But Granny was resolute. She liked the colors.

After some time trolling, Granny managed to hook into what seemed to be a huge fish, although certain members of the fishing party were sure it was a log or even another boat. Granny was a proud, even obstinate, woman and this onboard chatter had no bearing on her pursuit of the quarry. She spent a long hour struggling with the beast, and ultimately pulled it into the boat: a gigantic, warrior-like muskellunge. As the family picture shows, she was extremely proud of her catch, and in fact, for some time, held the record in that part of the world for great musky. There was even a local postcard of Granny with her fish. And once she had it in the boat, even Grandpa admitted that maybe she was correct in her lure selection. Unbeknownst to her, he certainly would have made an entry in his secret black book.

It was a well known fact on the island that Grandpa kept a logbook, yet even though people saw him taking notes, jotting down places, noting successes and even recording the first names of some of the river's fish, no one ever saw the inside of his log book. What fishing treasures must have been contained in its pages!

Soon after I met him and married his granddaughter, Grandpa passed away, moving on to a more peaceful river, perhaps. And that's when the trouble began, as his earthly goods were divided up. Some survivors received his furniture or cars. Others got stocks or bonds or ownership of his company. But what I wanted was his little black book. Personally, I could easily forgive Grandpa his decision to leave me out of the will; what was harder to take was the loss of that book. Keep the house, the cars, the stocks, the bonds, even the corporation. Just tell me where the fish have been hiding; tell me their desired time for luncheon reservations, their chosen menu, their favorite color, and how I should address them: with a formal Mister or Miss, with a title, a professional handle, their first name or a nickname?

As far as I have ever been able to figure out, no one ever found that fishing legacy. Granny has since passed on, with not a word about the book. And we have since spent a few days on the river with Grandpa's former fishing guide, a native American, who also denies having seen it. Every aunt, uncle, cousin and in-law has been consulted, and none of them admit to having the logbook. The general feeling seems to be that Grandpa found a way to sneak it into Heaven (and I would like to believe this).

There is one branch of the family that still keeps a place up on the island. They are protective of the area, and the rest of us are only invited up every five years or so for a family reunion, when it is too clamorous to dig about for lost treasure. But this branch of Grandpa's family tree is somewhat suspect in my mind — they don't even like fishing very much. Of all things, they use their Boston Whaler, a great fishing boat, for dragging water skiers around. And this boat, by the way, has a locked compartment on it.

They know of my passion for fishing, and always ask questions about my luck on the river. The only time they let me use the boat, however, the compartment was locked. In addition, they directed me to the same old spot, with too many sunnies and perch. I did have my revenge though. By appearing lost and confused, I found my own little spots... noted in a new little black book. One is a repeatedly productive bass hole, the other the former home of my impressive wall mount, Ike the Pike.

This log book is your chance to remember, your shot at leaving a meaningful legacy. Use it, enjoy it, reminisce with it. But please make sure that you designate a recipient for its contents when you pass on to that great stream in the sky.

EXPEDITIONS

🎣 LOCATION _____

CONDITIONS
DATE _____
TIME _____
WEATHER _____
TEMPERATURE _____

WATER
TEMPERATURE _____
CLARITY _____
DEPTH _____
TIDE _____

FLIES
PRESENTATION _____
COLOR _____
SIZE _____
PATTERN _____

FISH
SPECIES _____
NUMBER CAUGHT _____
LENGTH/GIRTH _____
WEIGHT _____

TACKLE
ROD _____
LINE _____
LEADER _____
WEIGHT _____

COMMENTS _____

🎣 LOCATION _____

CONDITIONS
DATE _____
TIME _____
WEATHER _____
TEMPERATURE _____

WATER
TEMPERATURE _____
CLARITY _____
DEPTH _____
TIDE _____

FLIES
PRESENTATION _____
COLOR _____
SIZE _____
PATTERN _____

FISH
SPECIES _____
NUMBER CAUGHT _____
LENGTH/GIRTH _____
WEIGHT _____

TACKLE
ROD _____
LINE _____
LEADER _____
WEIGHT _____

COMMENTS _____

🎣 9 🎣

EXPEDITIONS

LOCATION _____

CONDITIONS
DATE _____
TIME _____
WEATHER _____
TEMPERATURE _____

WATER
TEMPERATURE _____
CLARITY _____
DEPTH _____
TIDE _____

FLIES
PRESENTATION _____
COLOR _____
SIZE _____
PATTERN _____

FISH
SPECIES _____
NUMBER CAUGHT _____
LENGTH/GIRTH _____
WEIGHT _____

TACKLE
ROD _____
LINE _____
LEADER _____
WEIGHT _____

COMMENTS _____

LOCATION _____

CONDITIONS
DATE _____
TIME _____
WEATHER _____
TEMPERATURE _____

WATER
TEMPERATURE _____
CLARITY _____
DEPTH _____
TIDE _____

FLIES
PRESENTATION _____
COLOR _____
SIZE _____
PATTERN _____

FISH
SPECIES _____
NUMBER CAUGHT _____
LENGTH/GIRTH _____
WEIGHT _____

TACKLE
ROD _____
LINE _____
LEADER _____
WEIGHT _____

COMMENTS _____

EXPEDITIONS

❧ LOCATION _____

CONDITIONS
DATE _____
TIME _____
WEATHER _____
TEMPERATURE _____

WATER
TEMPERATURE _____
CLARITY _____
DEPTH _____
TIDE _____

FLIES
PRESENTATION _____
COLOR _____
SIZE _____
PATTERN _____

FISH
SPECIES _____
NUMBER CAUGHT _____
LENGTH/GIRTH _____
WEIGHT _____

TACKLE
ROD _____
LINE _____
LEADER _____
WEIGHT _____

COMMENTS _____

❧ LOCATION _____

CONDITIONS
DATE _____
TIME _____
WEATHER _____
TEMPERATURE _____

WATER
TEMPERATURE _____
CLARITY _____
DEPTH _____
TIDE _____

FLIES
PRESENTATION _____
COLOR _____
SIZE _____
PATTERN _____

FISH
SPECIES _____
NUMBER CAUGHT _____
LENGTH/GIRTH _____
WEIGHT _____

TACKLE
ROD _____
LINE _____
LEADER _____
WEIGHT _____

COMMENTS _____

EXPEDITIONS

🦟 LOCATION _____

CONDITIONS
DATE _____

TIME _____

WEATHER _____

TEMPERATURE _____

WATER
TEMPERATURE _____

CLARITY _____

DEPTH _____

TIDE _____

FLIES
PRESENTATION _____

COLOR _____

SIZE _____

PATTERN _____

FISH
SPECIES _____

NUMBER CAUGHT _____

LENGTH/GIRTH _____

WEIGHT _____

TACKLE
ROD _____

LINE _____

LEADER _____

WEIGHT _____

COMMENTS _____

🦟 LOCATION _____

CONDITIONS
DATE _____

TIME _____

WEATHER _____

TEMPERATURE _____

WATER
TEMPERATURE _____

CLARITY _____

DEPTH _____

TIDE _____

FLIES
PRESENTATION _____

COLOR _____

SIZE _____

PATTERN _____

FISH
SPECIES _____

NUMBER CAUGHT _____

LENGTH/GIRTH _____

WEIGHT _____

TACKLE
ROD _____

LINE _____

LEADER _____

WEIGHT _____

COMMENTS _____

*Potomantis, Yellow Spider on
John Quincy Adams logbook*

EXPEDITIONS

❧ LOCATION _____

CONDITIONS
DATE _____
TIME _____
WEATHER _____
TEMPERATURE _____

WATER
TEMPERATURE _____
CLARITY _____
DEPTH _____
TIDE _____

FLIES
PRESENTATION _____
COLOR _____
SIZE _____
PATTERN _____

FISH
SPECIES _____
NUMBER CAUGHT _____
LENGTH/GIRTH _____
WEIGHT _____

TACKLE
ROD _____
LINE _____
LEADER _____
WEIGHT _____

COMMENTS _____

❧ LOCATION _____

CONDITIONS
DATE _____
TIME _____
WEATHER _____
TEMPERATURE _____

WATER
TEMPERATURE _____
CLARITY _____
DEPTH _____
TIDE _____

FLIES
PRESENTATION _____
COLOR _____
SIZE _____
PATTERN _____

FISH
SPECIES _____
NUMBER CAUGHT _____
LENGTH/GIRTH _____
WEIGHT _____

TACKLE
ROD _____
LINE _____
LEADER _____
WEIGHT _____

COMMENTS _____

EXPEDITIONS

LOCATION _____

CONDITIONS	WATER	FLIES
DATE _____	TEMPERATURE _____	PRESENTATION _____
TIME _____	CLARITY _____	COLOR _____
WEATHER _____	DEPTH _____	SIZE _____
TEMPERATURE _____	TIDE _____	PATTERN _____

FISH	TACKLE
SPECIES _____	ROD _____
NUMBER CAUGHT _____	LINE _____
LENGTH/GIRTH _____	LEADER _____
WEIGHT _____	WEIGHT _____

COMMENTS_____

LOCATION _____

CONDITIONS	WATER	FLIES
DATE _____	TEMPERATURE _____	PRESENTATION _____
TIME _____	CLARITY _____	COLOR _____
WEATHER _____	DEPTH _____	SIZE _____
TEMPERATURE _____	TIDE _____	PATTERN _____

FISH	TACKLE
SPECIES _____	ROD _____
NUMBER CAUGHT _____	LINE _____
LENGTH/GIRTH _____	LEADER _____
WEIGHT _____	WEIGHT _____

COMMENTS_____

Stimulator Olive

EXPEDITIONS

🦟 LOCATION _____

CONDITIONS
DATE _____

TIME _____

WEATHER _____

TEMPERATURE _____

WATER
TEMPERATURE _____

CLARITY _____

DEPTH _____

TIDE _____

FLIES
PRESENTATION _____

COLOR _____

SIZE _____

PATTERN _____

FISH
SPECIES _____

NUMBER CAUGHT _____

LENGTH/GIRTH _____

WEIGHT _____

TACKLE
ROD _____

LINE _____

LEADER _____

WEIGHT _____

COMMENTS _____

🦟 LOCATION _____

CONDITIONS
DATE _____

TIME _____

WEATHER _____

TEMPERATURE _____

WATER
TEMPERATURE _____

CLARITY _____

DEPTH _____

TIDE _____

FLIES
PRESENTATION _____

COLOR _____

SIZE _____

PATTERN _____

FISH
SPECIES _____

NUMBER CAUGHT _____

LENGTH/GIRTH _____

WEIGHT _____

TACKLE
ROD _____

LINE _____

LEADER _____

WEIGHT _____

COMMENTS _____

Green Drake, wet, by Ed Hewitt

EXPEDITIONS

❧ LOCATION _____

CONDITIONS	WATER	FLIES
DATE _____	TEMPERATURE _____	PRESENTATION _____
TIME _____	CLARITY _____	COLOR _____
WEATHER _____	DEPTH _____	SIZE _____
TEMPERATURE _____	TIDE _____	PATTERN _____

FISH	TACKLE
SPECIES _____	ROD _____
NUMBER CAUGHT _____	LINE _____
LENGTH/GIRTH _____	LEADER _____
WEIGHT _____	WEIGHT _____

COMMENTS _____

❧ LOCATION _____

CONDITIONS	WATER	FLIES
DATE _____	TEMPERATURE _____	PRESENTATION _____
TIME _____	CLARITY _____	COLOR _____
WEATHER _____	DEPTH _____	SIZE _____
TEMPERATURE _____	TIDE _____	PATTERN _____

FISH	TACKLE
SPECIES _____	ROD _____
NUMBER CAUGHT _____	LINE _____
LENGTH/GIRTH _____	LEADER _____
WEIGHT _____	WEIGHT _____

COMMENTS _____

Lefty-Chartreuse Deceiver

EXPEDITIONS

LOCATION _____

CONDITIONS
DATE _____

TIME _____

WEATHER _____

TEMPERATURE _____

WATER
TEMPERATURE _____

CLARITY _____

DEPTH _____

TIDE _____

FLIES
PRESENTATION _____

COLOR _____

SIZE _____

PATTERN _____

FISH
SPECIES _____

NUMBER CAUGHT _____

LENGTH/GIRTH _____

WEIGHT _____

TACKLE
ROD _____

LINE _____

LEADER _____

WEIGHT _____

COMMENTS _____

LOCATION _____

CONDITIONS
DATE _____

TIME _____

WEATHER _____

TEMPERATURE _____

WATER
TEMPERATURE _____

CLARITY _____

DEPTH _____

TIDE _____

FLIES
PRESENTATION _____

COLOR _____

SIZE _____

PATTERN _____

FISH
SPECIES _____

NUMBER CAUGHT _____

LENGTH/GIRTH _____

WEIGHT _____

TACKLE
ROD _____

LINE _____

LEADER _____

WEIGHT _____

COMMENTS _____

EXPEDITIONS

❧ LOCATION _____

CONDITIONS
DATE _____
TIME _____
WEATHER _____
TEMPERATURE _____

WATER
TEMPERATURE _____
CLARITY _____
DEPTH _____
TIDE _____

FLIES
PRESENTATION _____
COLOR _____
SIZE _____
PATTERN _____

FISH
SPECIES _____
NUMBER CAUGHT _____
LENGTH/GIRTH _____
WEIGHT _____

TACKLE
ROD _____
LINE _____
LEADER _____
WEIGHT _____

COMMENTS _____

❧ LOCATION _____

CONDITIONS
DATE _____
TIME _____
WEATHER _____
TEMPERATURE _____

WATER
TEMPERATURE _____
CLARITY _____
DEPTH _____
TIDE _____

FLIES
PRESENTATION _____
COLOR _____
SIZE _____
PATTERN _____

FISH
SPECIES _____
NUMBER CAUGHT _____
LENGTH/GIRTH _____
WEIGHT _____

TACKLE
ROD _____
LINE _____
LEADER _____
WEIGHT _____

COMMENTS _____

Crazy Charlie's Bonefish

EXPEDITIONS

❧ LOCATION _____

CONDITIONS	WATER	FLIES
DATE _____	TEMPERATURE _____	PRESENTATION _____
TIME _____	CLARITY _____	COLOR _____
WEATHER _____	DEPTH _____	SIZE _____
TEMPERATURE _____	TIDE _____	PATTERN _____

FISH	TACKLE
SPECIES _____	ROD _____
NUMBER CAUGHT _____	LINE _____
LENGTH/GIRTH _____	LEADER _____
WEIGHT _____	WEIGHT _____

COMMENTS_____

❧ LOCATION _____

CONDITIONS	WATER	FLIES
DATE _____	TEMPERATURE _____	PRESENTATION _____
TIME _____	CLARITY _____	COLOR _____
WEATHER _____	DEPTH _____	SIZE _____
TEMPERATURE _____	TIDE _____	PATTERN _____

FISH	TACKLE
SPECIES _____	ROD _____
NUMBER CAUGHT _____	LINE _____
LENGTH/GIRTH _____	LEADER _____
WEIGHT _____	WEIGHT _____

COMMENTS_____

EXPEDITIONS

🪰 LOCATION _____

CONDITIONS	WATER	FLIES
DATE _____	TEMPERATURE _____	PRESENTATION _____
TIME _____	CLARITY _____	COLOR _____
WEATHER _____	DEPTH _____	SIZE _____
TEMPERATURE _____	TIDE _____	PATTERN _____

FISH	TACKLE
SPECIES _____	ROD _____
NUMBER CAUGHT _____	LINE _____
LENGTH/GIRTH _____	LEADER _____
WEIGHT _____	WEIGHT _____

COMMENTS _____

🪰 LOCATION _____

CONDITIONS	WATER	FLIES
DATE _____	TEMPERATURE _____	PRESENTATION _____
TIME _____	CLARITY _____	COLOR _____
WEATHER _____	DEPTH _____	SIZE _____
TEMPERATURE _____	TIDE _____	PATTERN _____

FISH	TACKLE
SPECIES _____	ROD _____
NUMBER CAUGHT _____	LINE _____
LENGTH/GIRTH _____	LEADER _____
WEIGHT _____	WEIGHT _____

COMMENTS _____

Black Dose

EXPEDITIONS

🐟 LOCATION _____

CONDITIONS
DATE _____
TIME _____
WEATHER _____
TEMPERATURE _____

WATER
TEMPERATURE _____
CLARITY _____
DEPTH _____
TIDE _____

FLIES
PRESENTATION _____
COLOR _____
SIZE _____
PATTERN _____

FISH
SPECIES _____
NUMBER CAUGHT _____
LENGTH/GIRTH _____
WEIGHT _____

TACKLE
ROD _____
LINE _____
LEADER _____
WEIGHT _____

COMMENTS _____

🐟 LOCATION _____

CONDITIONS
DATE _____
TIME _____
WEATHER _____
TEMPERATURE _____

WATER
TEMPERATURE _____
CLARITY _____
DEPTH _____
TIDE _____

FLIES
PRESENTATION _____
COLOR _____
SIZE _____
PATTERN _____

FISH
SPECIES _____
NUMBER CAUGHT _____
LENGTH/GIRTH _____
WEIGHT _____

TACKLE
ROD _____
LINE _____
LEADER _____
WEIGHT _____

COMMENTS _____

EXPEDITIONS

➤ LOCATION _____

CONDITIONS

DATE _____

TIME _____

WEATHER _____

TEMPERATURE _____

WATER

TEMPERATURE _____

CLARITY _____

DEPTH _____

TIDE _____

FLIES

PRESENTATION _____

COLOR _____

SIZE _____

PATTERN _____

FISH

SPECIES _____

NUMBER CAUGHT _____

LENGTH/GIRTH _____

WEIGHT _____

TACKLE

ROD _____

LINE _____

LEADER _____

WEIGHT _____

COMMENTS_____

➤ LOCATION _____

CONDITIONS

DATE _____

TIME _____

WEATHER _____

TEMPERATURE _____

WATER

TEMPERATURE _____

CLARITY _____

DEPTH _____

TIDE _____

FLIES

PRESENTATION _____

COLOR _____

SIZE _____

PATTERN _____

FISH

SPECIES _____

NUMBER CAUGHT _____

LENGTH/GIRTH _____

WEIGHT _____

TACKLE

ROD _____

LINE _____

LEADER _____

WEIGHT _____

COMMENTS_____

Bi-visible variant by Ed Hewitt

EXPEDITIONS

LOCATION _____

CONDITIONS
DATE _____
TIME _____
WEATHER _____
TEMPERATURE _____

WATER
TEMPERATURE _____
CLARITY _____
DEPTH _____
TIDE _____

FLIES
PRESENTATION _____
COLOR _____
SIZE _____
PATTERN _____

FISH
SPECIES _____
NUMBER CAUGHT _____
LENGTH/GIRTH _____
WEIGHT _____

TACKLE
ROD _____
LINE _____
LEADER _____
WEIGHT _____

COMMENTS _____

LOCATION _____

CONDITIONS
DATE _____
TIME _____
WEATHER _____
TEMPERATURE _____

WATER
TEMPERATURE _____
CLARITY _____
DEPTH _____
TIDE _____

FLIES
PRESENTATION _____
COLOR _____
SIZE _____
PATTERN _____

FISH
SPECIES _____
NUMBER CAUGHT _____
LENGTH/GIRTH _____
WEIGHT _____

TACKLE
ROD _____
LINE _____
LEADER _____
WEIGHT _____

COMMENTS _____

EXPEDITIONS

🦟 LOCATION _____

CONDITIONS
DATE _____
TIME _____
WEATHER _____
TEMPERATURE _____

WATER
TEMPERATURE _____
CLARITY _____
DEPTH _____
TIDE _____

FLIES
PRESENTATION _____
COLOR _____
SIZE _____
PATTERN _____

FISH
SPECIES _____
NUMBER CAUGHT _____
LENGTH/GIRTH _____
WEIGHT _____

TACKLE
ROD _____
LINE _____
LEADER _____
WEIGHT _____

COMMENTS _____

🦟 LOCATION _____

CONDITIONS
DATE _____
TIME _____
WEATHER _____
TEMPERATURE _____

WATER
TEMPERATURE _____
CLARITY _____
DEPTH _____
TIDE _____

FLIES
PRESENTATION _____
COLOR _____
SIZE _____
PATTERN _____

FISH
SPECIES _____
NUMBER CAUGHT _____
LENGTH/GIRTH _____
WEIGHT _____

TACKLE
ROD _____
LINE _____
LEADER _____
WEIGHT _____

COMMENTS _____

Butoric Sailfish

EXPEDITIONS

🎣 LOCATION _____

CONDITIONS	WATER	FLIES
DATE _____	TEMPERATURE _____	PRESENTATION _____
TIME _____	CLARITY _____	COLOR _____
WEATHER _____	DEPTH _____	SIZE _____
TEMPERATURE _____	TIDE _____	PATTERN _____

FISH	TACKLE
SPECIES _____	ROD _____
NUMBER CAUGHT _____	LINE _____
LENGTH/GIRTH _____	LEADER _____
WEIGHT _____	WEIGHT _____

COMMENTS _____

🎣 LOCATION _____

CONDITIONS	WATER	FLIES
DATE _____	TEMPERATURE _____	PRESENTATION _____
TIME _____	CLARITY _____	COLOR _____
WEATHER _____	DEPTH _____	SIZE _____
TEMPERATURE _____	TIDE _____	PATTERN _____

FISH	TACKLE
SPECIES _____	ROD _____
NUMBER CAUGHT _____	LINE _____
LENGTH/GIRTH _____	LEADER _____
WEIGHT _____	WEIGHT _____

COMMENTS _____

EXPEDITIONS

LOCATION _____

CONDITIONS
DATE _____
TIME _____
WEATHER _____
TEMPERATURE _____

WATER
TEMPERATURE _____
CLARITY _____
DEPTH _____
TIDE _____

FLIES
PRESENTATION _____
COLOR _____
SIZE _____
PATTERN _____

FISH
SPECIES _____
NUMBER CAUGHT _____
LENGTH/GIRTH _____
WEIGHT _____

TACKLE
ROD _____
LINE _____
LEADER _____
WEIGHT _____

COMMENTS_____

LOCATION _____

CONDITIONS
DATE _____
TIME _____
WEATHER _____
TEMPERATURE _____

WATER
TEMPERATURE _____
CLARITY _____
DEPTH _____
TIDE _____

FLIES
PRESENTATION _____
COLOR _____
SIZE _____
PATTERN _____

FISH
SPECIES _____
NUMBER CAUGHT _____
LENGTH/GIRTH _____
WEIGHT _____

TACKLE
ROD _____
LINE _____
LEADER _____
WEIGHT _____

COMMENTS_____

Yellow Humpy

EXPEDITIONS

❧ LOCATION _____

CONDITIONS
DATE _____
TIME _____
WEATHER _____
TEMPERATURE _____

WATER
TEMPERATURE _____
CLARITY _____
DEPTH _____
TIDE _____

FLIES
PRESENTATION _____
COLOR _____
SIZE _____
PATTERN _____

FISH
SPECIES _____
NUMBER CAUGHT _____
LENGTH/GIRTH _____
WEIGHT _____

TACKLE
ROD _____
LINE _____
LEADER _____
WEIGHT _____

COMMENTS _____

❧ LOCATION _____

CONDITIONS
DATE _____
TIME _____
WEATHER _____
TEMPERATURE _____

WATER
TEMPERATURE _____
CLARITY _____
DEPTH _____
TIDE _____

FLIES
PRESENTATION _____
COLOR _____
SIZE _____
PATTERN _____

FISH
SPECIES _____
NUMBER CAUGHT _____
LENGTH/GIRTH _____
WEIGHT _____

TACKLE
ROD _____
LINE _____
LEADER _____
WEIGHT _____

COMMENTS _____

Sparkle Zug Bug ❧ **45** ❧

EXPEDITIONS

❧ LOCATION _____

CONDITIONS
DATE _____
TIME _____
WEATHER _____
TEMPERATURE _____

WATER
TEMPERATURE _____
CLARITY _____
DEPTH _____
TIDE _____

FLIES
PRESENTATION _____
COLOR _____
SIZE _____
PATTERN _____

FISH
SPECIES _____
NUMBER CAUGHT _____
LENGTH/GIRTH _____
WEIGHT _____

TACKLE
ROD _____
LINE _____
LEADER _____
WEIGHT _____

COMMENTS _____

❧ LOCATION _____

CONDITIONS
DATE _____
TIME _____
WEATHER _____
TEMPERATURE _____

WATER
TEMPERATURE _____
CLARITY _____
DEPTH _____
TIDE _____

FLIES
PRESENTATION _____
COLOR _____
SIZE _____
PATTERN _____

FISH
SPECIES _____
NUMBER CAUGHT _____
LENGTH/GIRTH _____
WEIGHT _____

TACKLE
ROD _____
LINE _____
LEADER _____
WEIGHT _____

COMMENTS _____

MOE Bonefish Pink & Pearl

9-30-43

285th

Thursday, October 10

284th day — 8 days to c

air Cold
air 34
water 43

Otter flies. #8
Little #8 Silver #6
2 Bloodline #8

ked prol dype
le Brooke t.
iler) 3½# Gulce
Seder
tris ft
6

EXPEDITIONS

❧ LOCATION _____

CONDITIONS
DATE _____

TIME _____

WEATHER _____

TEMPERATURE _____

WATER
TEMPERATURE _____

CLARITY _____

DEPTH _____

TIDE _____

FLIES
PRESENTATION _____

COLOR _____

SIZE _____

PATTERN _____

FISH
SPECIES _____

NUMBER CAUGHT _____

LENGTH/GIRTH _____

WEIGHT _____

TACKLE
ROD _____

LINE _____

LEADER _____

WEIGHT _____

COMMENTS _____

❧ LOCATION _____

CONDITIONS
DATE _____

TIME _____

WEATHER _____

TEMPERATURE _____

WATER
TEMPERATURE _____

CLARITY _____

DEPTH _____

TIDE _____

FLIES
PRESENTATION _____

COLOR _____

SIZE _____

PATTERN _____

FISH
SPECIES _____

NUMBER CAUGHT _____

LENGTH/GIRTH _____

WEIGHT _____

TACKLE
ROD _____

LINE _____

LEADER _____

WEIGHT _____

COMMENTS _____

EXPEDITIONS

🦟 LOCATION _____

CONDITIONS
DATE _____
TIME _____
WEATHER _____
TEMPERATURE _____

WATER
TEMPERATURE _____
CLARITY _____
DEPTH _____
TIDE _____

FLIES
PRESENTATION _____
COLOR _____
SIZE _____
PATTERN _____

FISH
SPECIES _____
NUMBER CAUGHT _____
LENGTH/GIRTH _____
WEIGHT _____

TACKLE
ROD _____
LINE _____
LEADER _____
WEIGHT _____

COMMENTS _____

🦟 LOCATION _____

CONDITIONS
DATE _____
TIME _____
WEATHER _____
TEMPERATURE _____

WATER
TEMPERATURE _____
CLARITY _____
DEPTH _____
TIDE _____

FLIES
PRESENTATION _____
COLOR _____
SIZE _____
PATTERN _____

FISH
SPECIES _____
NUMBER CAUGHT _____
LENGTH/GIRTH _____
WEIGHT _____

TACKLE
ROD _____
LINE _____
LEADER _____
WEIGHT _____

COMMENTS _____

Hornberg Wet

EXPEDITIONS

🦋 LOCATION _____

CONDITIONS
DATE _____
TIME _____
WEATHER _____
TEMPERATURE _____

WATER
TEMPERATURE _____
CLARITY _____
DEPTH _____
TIDE _____

FLIES
PRESENTATION _____
COLOR _____
SIZE _____
PATTERN _____

FISH
SPECIES _____
NUMBER CAUGHT _____
LENGTH/GIRTH _____
WEIGHT _____

TACKLE
ROD _____
LINE _____
LEADER _____
WEIGHT _____

COMMENTS _____

🦋 LOCATION _____

CONDITIONS
DATE _____
TIME _____
WEATHER _____
TEMPERATURE _____

WATER
TEMPERATURE _____
CLARITY _____
DEPTH _____
TIDE _____

FLIES
PRESENTATION _____
COLOR _____
SIZE _____
PATTERN _____

FISH
SPECIES _____
NUMBER CAUGHT _____
LENGTH/GIRTH _____
WEIGHT _____

TACKLE
ROD _____
LINE _____
LEADER _____
WEIGHT _____

COMMENTS _____

EXPEDITIONS

✦ LOCATION _____

CONDITIONS
DATE _____
TIME _____
WEATHER _____
TEMPERATURE _____

WATER
TEMPERATURE _____
CLARITY _____
DEPTH _____
TIDE _____

FLIES
PRESENTATION _____
COLOR _____
SIZE _____
PATTERN _____

FISH
SPECIES _____
NUMBER CAUGHT _____
LENGTH/GIRTH _____
WEIGHT _____

TACKLE
ROD _____
LINE _____
LEADER _____
WEIGHT _____

COMMENTS _____

✦ LOCATION _____

CONDITIONS
DATE _____
TIME _____
WEATHER _____
TEMPERATURE _____

WATER
TEMPERATURE _____
CLARITY _____
DEPTH _____
TIDE _____

FLIES
PRESENTATION _____
COLOR _____
SIZE _____
PATTERN _____

FISH
SPECIES _____
NUMBER CAUGHT _____
LENGTH/GIRTH _____
WEIGHT _____

TACKLE
ROD _____
LINE _____
LEADER _____
WEIGHT _____

COMMENTS _____

Stone Fly nymph, by
Kevin MacEnerny

EXPEDITIONS

> LOCATION _____

CONDITIONS
DATE _____

TIME _____

WEATHER _____

TEMPERATURE _____

WATER
TEMPERATURE _____

CLARITY _____

DEPTH _____

TIDE _____

FLIES
PRESENTATION _____

COLOR _____

SIZE _____

PATTERN _____

FISH
SPECIES _____

NUMBER CAUGHT _____

LENGTH/GIRTH _____

WEIGHT _____

TACKLE
ROD _____

LINE _____

LEADER _____

WEIGHT _____

COMMENTS _____

> LOCATION _____

CONDITIONS
DATE _____

TIME _____

WEATHER _____

TEMPERATURE _____

WATER
TEMPERATURE _____

CLARITY _____

DEPTH _____

TIDE _____

FLIES
PRESENTATION _____

COLOR _____

SIZE _____

PATTERN _____

FISH
SPECIES _____

NUMBER CAUGHT _____

LENGTH/GIRTH _____

WEIGHT _____

TACKLE
ROD _____

LINE _____

LEADER _____

WEIGHT _____

COMMENTS _____

EXPEDITIONS

🎣 LOCATION _____

CONDITIONS
DATE _____
TIME _____
WEATHER _____
TEMPERATURE _____

WATER
TEMPERATURE _____
CLARITY _____
DEPTH _____
TIDE _____

FLIES
PRESENTATION _____
COLOR _____
SIZE _____
PATTERN _____

FISH
SPECIES _____
NUMBER CAUGHT _____
LENGTH/GIRTH _____
WEIGHT _____

TACKLE
ROD _____
LINE _____
LEADER _____
WEIGHT _____

COMMENTS _____

🎣 LOCATION _____

CONDITIONS
DATE _____
TIME _____
WEATHER _____
TEMPERATURE _____

WATER
TEMPERATURE _____
CLARITY _____
DEPTH _____
TIDE _____

FLIES
PRESENTATION _____
COLOR _____
SIZE _____
PATTERN _____

FISH
SPECIES _____
NUMBER CAUGHT _____
LENGTH/GIRTH _____
WEIGHT _____

TACKLE
ROD _____
LINE _____
LEADER _____
WEIGHT _____

COMMENTS _____

Schoolie - Sand eel

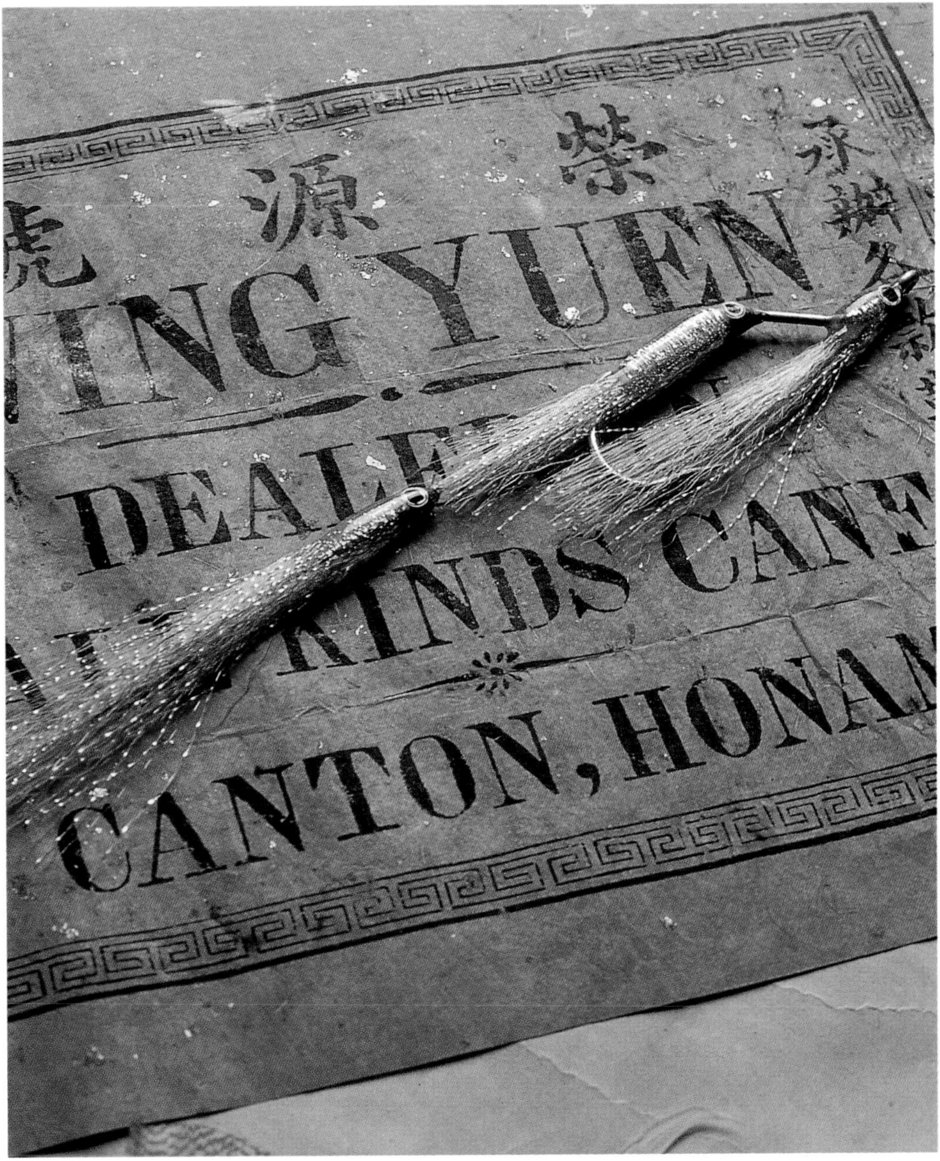
源 榮
ING YUEN
DEAL
KINDS CANE
CANTON, HONAM

EXPEDITIONS

❧ LOCATION _____

CONDITIONS	WATER	FLIES
DATE _____	TEMPERATURE _____	PRESENTATION _____
TIME _____	CLARITY _____	COLOR _____
WEATHER _____	DEPTH _____	SIZE _____
TEMPERATURE _____	TIDE _____	PATTERN _____

FISH	TACKLE
SPECIES _____	ROD _____
NUMBER CAUGHT _____	LINE _____
LENGTH/GIRTH _____	LEADER _____
WEIGHT _____	WEIGHT _____

COMMENTS_____

❧ LOCATION _____

CONDITIONS	WATER	FLIES
DATE _____	TEMPERATURE _____	PRESENTATION _____
TIME _____	CLARITY _____	COLOR _____
WEATHER _____	DEPTH _____	SIZE _____
TEMPERATURE _____	TIDE _____	PATTERN _____

FISH	TACKLE
SPECIES _____	ROD _____
NUMBER CAUGHT _____	LINE _____
LENGTH/GIRTH _____	LEADER _____
WEIGHT _____	WEIGHT _____

COMMENTS_____

EXPEDITIONS

❧ LOCATION _____

CONDITIONS	WATER	FLIES
DATE _____	TEMPERATURE _____	PRESENTATION _____
TIME _____	CLARITY _____	COLOR _____
WEATHER _____	DEPTH _____	SIZE _____
TEMPERATURE _____	TIDE _____	PATTERN _____

FISH	TACKLE
SPECIES _____	ROD _____
NUMBER CAUGHT _____	LINE _____
LENGTH/GIRTH _____	LEADER _____
WEIGHT _____	WEIGHT _____

COMMENTS _____

❧ LOCATION _____

CONDITIONS	WATER	FLIES
DATE _____	TEMPERATURE _____	PRESENTATION _____
TIME _____	CLARITY _____	COLOR _____
WEATHER _____	DEPTH _____	SIZE _____
TEMPERATURE _____	TIDE _____	PATTERN _____

FISH	TACKLE
SPECIES _____	ROD _____
NUMBER CAUGHT _____	LINE _____
LENGTH/GIRTH _____	LEADER _____
WEIGHT _____	WEIGHT _____

COMMENTS _____

Mickey Finn

EXPEDITIONS

LOCATION _____

CONDITIONS
DATE _____

TIME _____

WEATHER _____

TEMPERATURE _____

WATER
TEMPERATURE _____

CLARITY _____

DEPTH _____

TIDE _____

FLIES
PRESENTATION _____

COLOR _____

SIZE _____

PATTERN _____

FISH
SPECIES _____

NUMBER CAUGHT _____

LENGTH/GIRTH _____

WEIGHT _____

TACKLE
ROD _____

LINE _____

LEADER _____

WEIGHT _____

COMMENTS_____

LOCATION _____

CONDITIONS
DATE _____

TIME _____

WEATHER _____

TEMPERATURE _____

WATER
TEMPERATURE _____

CLARITY _____

DEPTH _____

TIDE _____

FLIES
PRESENTATION _____

COLOR _____

SIZE _____

PATTERN _____

FISH
SPECIES _____

NUMBER CAUGHT _____

LENGTH/GIRTH _____

WEIGHT _____

TACKLE
ROD _____

LINE _____

LEADER _____

WEIGHT _____

COMMENTS_____

EXPEDITIONS

🪰 LOCATION _____

CONDITIONS
DATE _____

TIME _____

WEATHER _____

TEMPERATURE _____

WATER
TEMPERATURE _____

CLARITY _____

DEPTH _____

TIDE _____

FLIES
PRESENTATION _____

COLOR _____

SIZE _____

PATTERN _____

FISH
SPECIES _____

NUMBER CAUGHT _____

LENGTH/GIRTH _____

WEIGHT _____

TACKLE
ROD _____

LINE _____

LEADER _____

WEIGHT _____

COMMENTS _____

🪰 LOCATION _____

CONDITIONS
DATE _____

TIME _____

WEATHER _____

TEMPERATURE _____

WATER
TEMPERATURE _____

CLARITY _____

DEPTH _____

TIDE _____

FLIES
PRESENTATION _____

COLOR _____

SIZE _____

PATTERN _____

FISH
SPECIES _____

NUMBER CAUGHT _____

LENGTH/GIRTH _____

WEIGHT _____

TACKLE
ROD _____

LINE _____

LEADER _____

WEIGHT _____

COMMENTS _____

Weber Dylite Popper Body

EXPEDITIONS

🎣 LOCATION _____

CONDITIONS

DATE _____

TIME _____

WEATHER _____

TEMPERATURE _____

WATER

TEMPERATURE _____

CLARITY _____

DEPTH _____

TIDE _____

FLIES

PRESENTATION _____

COLOR _____

SIZE _____

PATTERN _____

FISH

SPECIES _____

NUMBER CAUGHT _____

LENGTH/GIRTH _____

WEIGHT _____

TACKLE

ROD _____

LINE _____

LEADER _____

WEIGHT _____

COMMENTS _____

🎣 LOCATION _____

CONDITIONS

DATE _____

TIME _____

WEATHER _____

TEMPERATURE _____

WATER

TEMPERATURE _____

CLARITY _____

DEPTH _____

TIDE _____

FLIES

PRESENTATION _____

COLOR _____

SIZE _____

PATTERN _____

FISH

SPECIES _____

NUMBER CAUGHT _____

LENGTH/GIRTH _____

WEIGHT _____

TACKLE

ROD _____

LINE _____

LEADER _____

WEIGHT _____

COMMENTS _____

EXPEDITIONS

> LOCATION _____

CONDITIONS
DATE _____

TIME _____

WEATHER _____

TEMPERATURE _____

WATER
TEMPERATURE _____

CLARITY _____

DEPTH _____

TIDE _____

FLIES
PRESENTATION _____

COLOR _____

SIZE _____

PATTERN _____

FISH
SPECIES _____

NUMBER CAUGHT _____

LENGTH/GIRTH _____

WEIGHT _____

TACKLE
ROD _____

LINE _____

LEADER _____

WEIGHT _____

COMMENTS_____

> LOCATION _____

CONDITIONS
DATE _____

TIME _____

WEATHER _____

TEMPERATURE _____

WATER
TEMPERATURE _____

CLARITY _____

DEPTH _____

TIDE _____

FLIES
PRESENTATION _____

COLOR _____

SIZE _____

PATTERN _____

FISH
SPECIES _____

NUMBER CAUGHT _____

LENGTH/GIRTH _____

WEIGHT _____

TACKLE
ROD _____

LINE _____

LEADER _____

WEIGHT _____

COMMENTS_____

Dry Rind Frog

EXPEDITIONS

🎣 LOCATION _____

CONDITIONS
DATE _____
TIME _____
WEATHER _____
TEMPERATURE _____

WATER
TEMPERATURE _____
CLARITY _____
DEPTH _____
TIDE _____

FLIES
PRESENTATION _____
COLOR _____
SIZE _____
PATTERN _____

FISH
SPECIES _____
NUMBER CAUGHT _____
LENGTH/GIRTH _____
WEIGHT _____

TACKLE
ROD _____
LINE _____
LEADER _____
WEIGHT _____

COMMENTS _____

🎣 LOCATION _____

CONDITIONS
DATE _____
TIME _____
WEATHER _____
TEMPERATURE _____

WATER
TEMPERATURE _____
CLARITY _____
DEPTH _____
TIDE _____

FLIES
PRESENTATION _____
COLOR _____
SIZE _____
PATTERN _____

FISH
SPECIES _____
NUMBER CAUGHT _____
LENGTH/GIRTH _____
WEIGHT _____

TACKLE
ROD _____
LINE _____
LEADER _____
WEIGHT _____

COMMENTS _____

Prince, weighted

Expeditions

❧ LOCATION _____

CONDITIONS
DATE _____

TIME _____

WEATHER _____

TEMPERATURE _____

WATER
TEMPERATURE _____

CLARITY _____

DEPTH _____

TIDE _____

FLIES
PRESENTATION _____

COLOR _____

SIZE _____

PATTERN _____

FISH
SPECIES _____

NUMBER CAUGHT _____

LENGTH/GIRTH _____

WEIGHT _____

TACKLE
ROD _____

LINE _____

LEADER _____

WEIGHT _____

COMMENTS_____

❧ LOCATION _____

CONDITIONS
DATE _____

TIME _____

WEATHER _____

TEMPERATURE _____

WATER
TEMPERATURE _____

CLARITY _____

DEPTH _____

TIDE _____

FLIES
PRESENTATION _____

COLOR _____

SIZE _____

PATTERN _____

FISH
SPECIES _____

NUMBER CAUGHT _____

LENGTH/GIRTH _____

WEIGHT _____

TACKLE
ROD _____

LINE _____

LEADER _____

WEIGHT _____

COMMENTS_____

Mann's Smelt

EXPEDITIONS

LOCATION _____

CONDITIONS	WATER	FLIES
DATE _____	TEMPERATURE _____	PRESENTATION _____
TIME _____	CLARITY _____	COLOR _____
WEATHER _____	DEPTH _____	SIZE _____
TEMPERATURE _____	TIDE _____	PATTERN _____

FISH	TACKLE
SPECIES _____	ROD _____
NUMBER CAUGHT _____	LINE _____
LENGTH/GIRTH _____	LEADER _____
WEIGHT _____	WEIGHT _____

COMMENTS_____

LOCATION _____

CONDITIONS	WATER	FLIES
DATE _____	TEMPERATURE _____	PRESENTATION _____
TIME _____	CLARITY _____	COLOR _____
WEATHER _____	DEPTH _____	SIZE _____
TEMPERATURE _____	TIDE _____	PATTERN _____

FISH	TACKLE
SPECIES _____	ROD _____
NUMBER CAUGHT _____	LINE _____
LENGTH/GIRTH _____	LEADER _____
WEIGHT _____	WEIGHT _____

COMMENTS_____

EXPEDITIONS

🐟 LOCATION _____

CONDITIONS
DATE _____
TIME _____
WEATHER _____
TEMPERATURE _____

WATER
TEMPERATURE _____
CLARITY _____
DEPTH _____
TIDE _____

FLIES
PRESENTATION _____
COLOR _____
SIZE _____
PATTERN _____

FISH
SPECIES _____
NUMBER CAUGHT _____
LENGTH/GIRTH _____
WEIGHT _____

TACKLE
ROD _____
LINE _____
LEADER _____
WEIGHT _____

COMMENTS _____

🐟 LOCATION _____

CONDITIONS
DATE _____
TIME _____
WEATHER _____
TEMPERATURE _____

WATER
TEMPERATURE _____
CLARITY _____
DEPTH _____
TIDE _____

FLIES
PRESENTATION _____
COLOR _____
SIZE _____
PATTERN _____

FISH
SPECIES _____
NUMBER CAUGHT _____
LENGTH/GIRTH _____
WEIGHT _____

TACKLE
ROD _____
LINE _____
LEADER _____
WEIGHT _____

COMMENTS _____

Bead Head Minnow

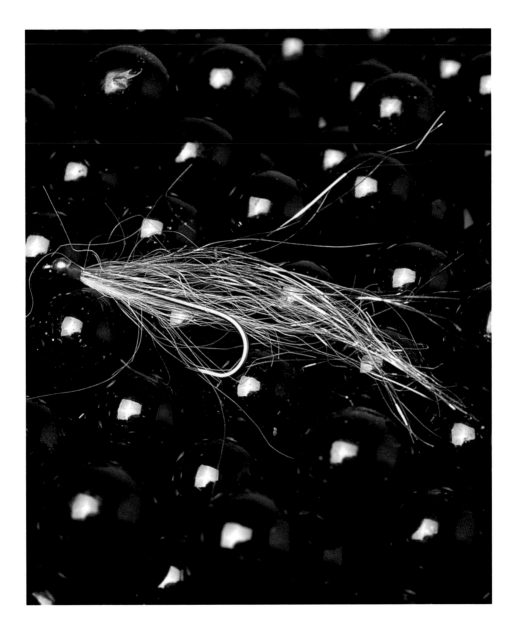

EXPEDITIONS

🪰 LOCATION _____

CONDITIONS
DATE _____

TIME _____

WEATHER _____

TEMPERATURE _____

WATER
TEMPERATURE _____

CLARITY _____

DEPTH _____

TIDE _____

FLIES
PRESENTATION _____

COLOR _____

SIZE _____

PATTERN _____

FISH
SPECIES _____

NUMBER CAUGHT _____

LENGTH/GIRTH _____

WEIGHT _____

TACKLE
ROD _____

LINE _____

LEADER _____

WEIGHT _____

COMMENTS_____

🪰 LOCATION _____

CONDITIONS
DATE _____

TIME _____

WEATHER _____

TEMPERATURE _____

WATER
TEMPERATURE _____

CLARITY _____

DEPTH _____

TIDE _____

FLIES
PRESENTATION _____

COLOR _____

SIZE _____

PATTERN _____

FISH
SPECIES _____

NUMBER CAUGHT _____

LENGTH/GIRTH _____

WEIGHT _____

TACKLE
ROD _____

LINE _____

LEADER _____

WEIGHT _____

COMMENTS_____

EXPEDITIONS

❧ LOCATION _____

CONDITIONS
DATE _____

TIME _____

WEATHER _____

TEMPERATURE _____

WATER
TEMPERATURE _____

CLARITY _____

DEPTH _____

TIDE _____

FLIES
PRESENTATION _____

COLOR _____

SIZE _____

PATTERN _____

FISH
SPECIES _____

NUMBER CAUGHT _____

LENGTH/GIRTH _____

WEIGHT _____

TACKLE
ROD _____

LINE _____

LEADER _____

WEIGHT _____

COMMENTS_____

❧ LOCATION _____

CONDITIONS
DATE _____

TIME _____

WEATHER _____

TEMPERATURE _____

WATER
TEMPERATURE _____

CLARITY _____

DEPTH _____

TIDE _____

FLIES
PRESENTATION _____

COLOR _____

SIZE _____

PATTERN _____

FISH
SPECIES _____

NUMBER CAUGHT _____

LENGTH/GIRTH _____

WEIGHT _____

TACKLE
ROD _____

LINE _____

LEADER _____

WEIGHT _____

COMMENTS_____

EXPEDITIONS

LOCATION _____

CONDITIONS
DATE _____

TIME _____

WEATHER _____

TEMPERATURE _____

WATER
TEMPERATURE _____

CLARITY _____

DEPTH _____

TIDE _____

FLIES
PRESENTATION _____

COLOR _____

SIZE _____

PATTERN _____

FISH
SPECIES _____

NUMBER CAUGHT _____

LENGTH/GIRTH _____

WEIGHT _____

TACKLE
ROD _____

LINE _____

LEADER _____

WEIGHT _____

COMMENTS _____

LOCATION _____

CONDITIONS
DATE _____

TIME _____

WEATHER _____

TEMPERATURE _____

WATER
TEMPERATURE _____

CLARITY _____

DEPTH _____

TIDE _____

FLIES
PRESENTATION _____

COLOR _____

SIZE _____

PATTERN _____

FISH
SPECIES _____

NUMBER CAUGHT _____

LENGTH/GIRTH _____

WEIGHT _____

TACKLE
ROD _____

LINE _____

LEADER _____

WEIGHT _____

COMMENTS _____

Launch Sites

Location

NAME _____ TELEPHONE _____

ADDRESS _____

_____

DIRECTIONS _____

Marina _____

FACILITIES _____

COURSE _____

DISTANCE _____

NAVIGATION GUIDES _____

Comments _____

Location

NAME _____ TELEPHONE _____

ADDRESS _____

_____

DIRECTIONS _____

Marina _____

FACILITIES _____

COURSE _____

DISTANCE _____

NAVIGATION GUIDES _____

Comments _____

Classic Atlantic Salmon Fly,
by Dorothy Douglas

LAUNCH SITES

LOCATION

NAME _____ TELEPHONE _____

ADDRESS _____

_____

DIRECTIONS _____

MARINA _____

FACILITIES _____

COURSE _____

DISTANCE _____

NAVIGATION GUIDES _____

COMMENTS _____

LOCATION

NAME _____ TELEPHONE _____

ADDRESS _____

_____

DIRECTIONS _____

MARINA _____

FACILITIES _____

COURSE _____

DISTANCE _____

NAVIGATION GUIDES _____

COMMENTS _____

LAUNCH SITES

🦋 LOCATION

NAME _____ TELEPHONE _____

ADDRESS _____

_____

DIRECTIONS _____

MARINA _____

FACILITIES _____

COURSE _____

DISTANCE _____

NAVIGATION GUIDES _____

COMMENTS _____

🦋 LOCATION

NAME _____ TELEPHONE _____

ADDRESS _____

_____

DIRECTIONS _____

MARINA _____

FACILITIES _____

COURSE _____

DISTANCE _____

NAVIGATION GUIDES _____

COMMENTS _____

Launch Sites

❧ LOCATION

NAME _____ TELEPHONE _____

ADDRESS _____

_____

DIRECTIONS _____

MARINA _____

FACILITIES _____

COURSE _____

DISTANCE _____

NAVIGATION GUIDES _____

COMMENTS _____

❧ LOCATION

NAME _____ TELEPHONE _____

ADDRESS _____

_____

DIRECTIONS _____

MARINA _____

FACILITIES _____

COURSE _____

DISTANCE _____

NAVIGATION GUIDES _____

COMMENTS _____

LAUNCH SITES

❧ LOCATION

NAME _____ TELEPHONE _____

ADDRESS _____

_____

DIRECTIONS _____

MARINA _____

FACILITIES _____

COURSE _____

DISTANCE _____

NAVIGATION GUIDES _____

COMMENTS _____

❧ LOCATION

NAME _____ TELEPHONE _____

ADDRESS _____

_____

DIRECTIONS _____

MARINA _____

FACILITIES _____

COURSE _____

DISTANCE _____

NAVIGATION GUIDES _____

COMMENTS _____

LAUNCH SITES

LOCATION

NAME _____ TELEPHONE _____

ADDRESS _____

_____

DIRECTIONS _____

MARINA _____

FACILITIES _____

COURSE _____

DISTANCE _____

NAVIGATION GUIDES _____

COMMENTS _____

LOCATION

NAME _____ TELEPHONE _____

ADDRESS _____

_____

DIRECTIONS _____

MARINA _____

FACILITIES _____

COURSE _____

DISTANCE _____

NAVIGATION GUIDES _____

COMMENTS _____

Launch Sites

Location

NAME _____ TELEPHONE _____

ADDRESS _____

_____

DIRECTIONS _____

Marina _____

FACILITIES _____

COURSE _____

DISTANCE _____

NAVIGATION GUIDES _____

Comments _____

Location

NAME _____ TELEPHONE _____

ADDRESS _____

_____

DIRECTIONS _____

Marina _____

FACILITIES _____

COURSE _____

DISTANCE _____

NAVIGATION GUIDES _____

Comments _____

Launch Sites

❧ Location

NAME _____ TELEPHONE _____

ADDRESS _____

_____

DIRECTIONS _____

Marina _____

FACILITIES _____

COURSE _____

DISTANCE _____

NAVIGATION GUIDES _____

Comments _____

❧ Location

NAME _____ TELEPHONE _____

ADDRESS _____

_____

DIRECTIONS _____

Marina _____

FACILITIES _____

COURSE _____

DISTANCE _____

NAVIGATION GUIDES _____

Comments _____

LAUNCH SITES

🦋 LOCATION

NAME _____ TELEPHONE _____

ADDRESS _____

_____

DIRECTIONS _____

MARINA _____

FACILITIES _____

COURSE _____

DISTANCE _____

NAVIGATION GUIDES _____

COMMENTS _____

🦋 LOCATION

NAME _____ TELEPHONE _____

ADDRESS _____

_____

DIRECTIONS _____

MARINA _____

FACILITIES _____

COURSE _____

DISTANCE _____

NAVIGATION GUIDES _____

COMMENTS _____

ut

rge

George Tries the Black

Above the Gorge

FLY ✤ FISHING PARTNERS

NAME _____

ADDRESS _____
_____

PHONE (H) _____ PHONE (W) _____ FAX _____

TACKLE _____

COMMENTS _____

NAME _____

ADDRESS _____
_____

PHONE (H) _____ PHONE (W) _____ FAX _____

TACKLE _____

COMMENTS _____

NAME _____

ADDRESS _____
_____

PHONE (H) _____ PHONE (W) _____ FAX _____

TACKLE _____

COMMENTS _____

*Built Wing Classic Salmon
Fly, by William Chandler*

FLY ✦ FISHING PARTNERS

✦ NAME _____

ADDRESS _____
_____

PHONE (H) _____ PHONE (W) _____ FAX _____

TACKLE _____

COMMENTS _____

✦ NAME _____

ADDRESS _____
_____

PHONE (H) _____ PHONE (W) _____ FAX _____

TACKLE _____

COMMENTS _____

✦ NAME _____

ADDRESS _____
_____

PHONE (H) _____ PHONE (W) _____ FAX _____

TACKLE _____

COMMENTS _____

FLY ✦ FISHING PARTNERS

🪰 NAME _____

ADDRESS _____

_____

PHONE (H) _____ PHONE (W) _____ FAX _____

TACKLE _____

COMMENTS _____

🪰 NAME _____

ADDRESS _____

_____

PHONE (H) _____ PHONE (W) _____ FAX _____

TACKLE _____

COMMENTS _____

🪰 NAME _____

ADDRESS _____

_____

PHONE (H) _____ PHONE (W) _____ FAX _____

TACKLE _____

COMMENTS _____

FLY ✤ FISHING PARTNERS

✤ NAME _____

ADDRESS _____

_____

PHONE (H) _____ PHONE (W) _____ FAX _____

TACKLE _____

COMMENTS _____

✤ NAME _____

ADDRESS _____

_____

PHONE (H) _____ PHONE (W) _____ FAX _____

TACKLE _____

COMMENTS _____

✤ NAME _____

ADDRESS _____

_____

PHONE (H) _____ PHONE (W) _____ FAX _____

TACKLE _____

COMMENTS _____

Fly ❧ fishing Partners

❧ NAME _____

ADDRESS _____

_____

PHONE (H) _____ PHONE (W) _____ FAX _____

TACKLE _____

COMMENTS _____

❧ NAME _____

ADDRESS _____

_____

PHONE (H) _____ PHONE (W) _____ FAX _____

TACKLE _____

COMMENTS _____

❧ NAME _____

ADDRESS _____

_____

PHONE (H) _____ PHONE (W) _____ FAX _____

TACKLE _____

COMMENTS _____

FLY ❧ FISHING PARTNERS

❧ NAME _____

ADDRESS _____

_____

PHONE (H) _____ PHONE (W) _____ FAX _____

TACKLE _____

COMMENTS _____

❧ NAME _____

ADDRESS _____

_____

PHONE (H) _____ PHONE (W) _____ FAX _____

TACKLE _____

COMMENTS _____

❧ NAME _____

ADDRESS _____

_____

PHONE (H) _____ PHONE (W) _____ FAX _____

TACKLE _____

COMMENTS _____

FLY ✢ FISHING PARTNERS

✤ NAME _____
ADDRESS _____
_____
PHONE (H) _____ PHONE (W) _____ FAX _____
TACKLE _____
COMMENTS _____

✤ NAME _____
ADDRESS _____
_____
PHONE (H) _____ PHONE (W) _____ FAX _____
TACKLE _____
COMMENTS _____

✤ NAME _____
ADDRESS _____
_____
PHONE (H) _____ PHONE (W) _____ FAX _____
TACKLE _____
COMMENTS _____

FLY ➤ FISHING PARTNERS

➤ NAME _____

ADDRESS _____
_____

PHONE (H) _____ PHONE (W) _____ FAX _____

TACKLE _____

COMMENTS _____

➤ NAME _____

ADDRESS _____
_____

PHONE (H) _____ PHONE (W) _____ FAX _____

TACKLE _____

COMMENTS _____

➤ NAME _____

ADDRESS _____
_____

PHONE (H) _____ PHONE (W) _____ FAX _____

TACKLE _____

COMMENTS _____

FLY ❧ FISHING PARTNERS

❧ NAME _____

ADDRESS _____

_____

PHONE (H) _____ PHONE (W) _____ FAX _____

TACKLE _____

COMMENTS _____

❧ NAME _____

ADDRESS _____

_____

PHONE (H) _____ PHONE (W) _____ FAX _____

TACKLE _____

COMMENTS _____

❧ NAME _____

ADDRESS _____

_____

PHONE (H) _____ PHONE (W) _____ FAX _____

TACKLE _____

COMMENTS _____

FLY ✥ FISHING PARTNERS

✥ NAME _____

ADDRESS _____

_____

PHONE (H) _____ PHONE (W) _____ FAX _____

TACKLE _____

COMMENTS _____

✥ NAME _____

ADDRESS _____

_____

PHONE (H) _____ PHONE (W) _____ FAX _____

TACKLE _____

COMMENTS _____

✥ NAME _____

ADDRESS _____

_____

PHONE (H) _____ PHONE (W) _____ FAX _____

TACKLE _____

COMMENTS _____

Fly-fishing Partners

Name _____

ADDRESS _____

_____

PHONE (H) _____ PHONE (W) _____ FAX _____

TACKLE _____

Comments _____

Name _____

ADDRESS _____

_____

PHONE (H) _____ PHONE (W) _____ FAX _____

TACKLE _____

Comments _____

Name _____

ADDRESS _____

_____

PHONE (H) _____ PHONE (W) _____ FAX _____

TACKLE _____

Comments _____

SUPPLIES & EQUIPMENT

AMERICAN ANGLING SUPPLY
23 Main Street • Salem, New Hampshire 03079
1•603•893•3333 or 1•800•Angler•8

CABELA'S
812-13th Avenue • Sidney, Nebraska 69160
1•800•237•8888

L.L.BEAN
Order Department • L.L. Street • Freeport, Maine 04033
1•800•341•4341

THE ORVIS COMPANY, INCORPORATED
Historic Route 7A • Manchester, Vermont 05254
1•800•548•9548

UMPQUA FEATHERS MERCHANTS
P.O. Box 700 • Glide, Oregon 97443
1•800•322•3218 or 1•503•496•3512

CONSERVATION ORGANIZATIONS

BRITISH FIELD SPORTS ASSOCIATION
59 Kennington Road • London SE1 7PZ
071•928•4742

SALMON AND TROUT ASSOCIATION
Fishmongers Hall • London Bridge • London EC4 R9EL
071•283•5838

THE ATLANTIC SALMON FEDERATION
P.O. Box 429 • St. Andrews • New Brunswick, Canada EOG 2XO
1•506•529•4581
P.O. Box 807 • Calais, Maine 04619
1•506•529•4581

THE FEDERATION OF FLY FISHERS
P.O. Box 1595 • Bozeman, Montana 59771
1•800•618•0808

TROUT UNLIMITED
1500 Wilson Blvd., Suite 310 • Arlington, Virginia 22209-2310
1•703•522•0200

*Hand woven hair fly, by
Pott family*

KNOTS

BLOOD KNOT

Use to tie tippet to end of leader or to join sections of tapered leaders.

Cross both pieces of material in an "X", leaving at least 8" of overlap.

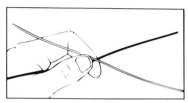

Wind one end around the standing part of the other piece five times and pass the end on the other side of the "X" formed by the intersection of the two pieces.

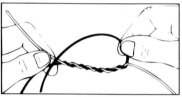

Pinch the line at this point and with the other hand wind the free end around the standing piece in the opposite direction five times. Pass this end through the same loop as the first end, but go through the loop in the opposite direction.

Lubricate and hold both ends together while pulling on the standing parts to tighten. The easiest way to keep the ends from slipping through is to hold them in your teeth. Don't put any pressure on the short ends while tightening.

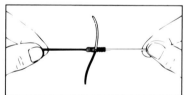

Trim tag ends as close to the knot as possible.

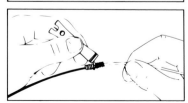

KNOTS

CLINCH KNOT

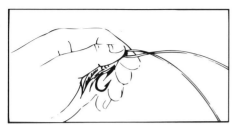

USE TO TIE FLY TO END OF TIPPET. SOMETIMES TIED AS AN "IMPROVED" CLINCH KNOT BY PASSING THE TAG END BACK THROUGH THE LOOP CREATED AT THE END OF STEP NUMBER THREE.

INSERT 6" TO 8" OF TIPPET THROUGH EYE OF HOOK.

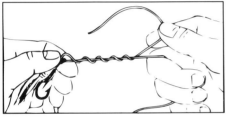

HOLD FLY IN LEFT HAND AND WITH RIGHT HAND WIND THE END OF THE LEADER AROUND STANDING PART OF LEADER FIVE TIMES, KEEPING A SMALL LOOP IMMEDIATELY ADJACENT TO HOOK EYE OPEN. THIS LOOP IS EASY TO KEEP OPEN IF YOU PINCH IT BETWEEN THUMB AND FOREFINGER OF LEFT HAND.

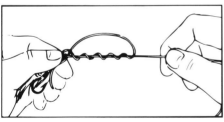

BRING TAG END OF LEADER THROUGH LOOP NEXT TO THE HOOK EYE AND GRASP WITH THUMB AND FOREFINGER OF LEFT HAND.

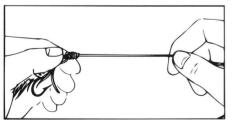

LUBRICATE AND TIGHTEN BY PULLING THE STANDING PART OF LEADER AND THE FLY IN OPPOSITE DIRECTIONS. DO NOT PULL ON THE TAG END OF THE LEADER—MERELY HOLD IT ALONGSIDE THE FLY. TRIM TAG END CLOSE TO KNOT.

SURGEON'S LOOP

THE SURGEON'S LOOP IS USED TO TIE LOOP IN END OF LEADER.

FORM A LOOP IN THE END OF LEADER.

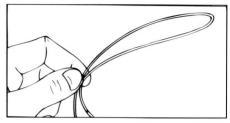

MAKE A SIMPLE OVERHAND KNOT IN THE DOUBLE LINE.

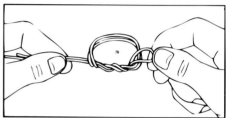

THEN BRING THE LOOP END THROUGH THE OVERHAND KNOT AGAIN. LUBRICATE AND TIGHTEN BY PULLING ON THE LOOP END WITH ONE HAND AND THE STANDING LEADER AND TAG END IN THE OTHER.

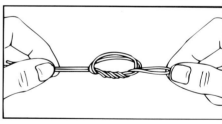

TRIM.

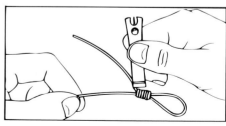

KNOTS

UNI-KNOT

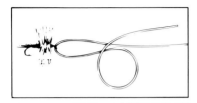

USE TO TIE FLY TO TIPPET. CREATES A SLIDING LOOP THAT CAN BE LEFT OPEN OR TIGHTENED AGAINST HOOK EYE. THIS LOOP LETS NYMPHS AND OTHER SUBSURFACE FLIES "SWIM" IN THE WATER AND BASS BUGS POP BETTER.

PASS 6" TO 8" OF TAG END OF TIPPET THROUGH THE EYE OF HOOK. FORM A 1½" DIAMETER LOOP WITH TAG END.

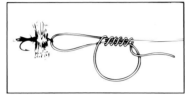

PASS TAG THROUGH AND AROUND LOOP AND TIPPET FIVE TIMES, MOVING AWAY FROM FLY.

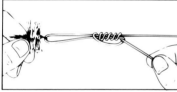

LUBRICATE AND TIGHTEN KNOT BY PULLING VERY TIGHTLY ON TAG END. THE DEGREE OF TIGHTENING DETERMINES HOW KNOT SLIDES ON TIPPET FOR KEEPING LOOP OPEN OR SLIDING IT CLOSED. WITH HEAVY TIPPET MATERIAL (OVER .011"), GRASP THE TAG END WITH PLIERS OR HEMOSTATS AND TIGHTEN THE KNOT.

ADJUST LOOP BETWEEN FLY AND KNOT AS DESIRED. TRIM TAG END.

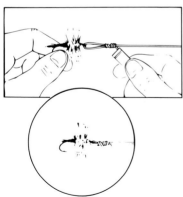

ACKNOWLEDGEMENTS

We are indebted to the American Museum of Fly Fishing for use of their collection of flies and fly-fishing paraphernalia. The A.M.F.F., a nonprofit, educational institution dedicated to preserving the rich heritage of fly fishing serves as a repository for, and conservator to, the world's largest collection of angling-related objects. For further information contact: The American Museum of Fly Fishing, P.O. Box 42, Manchester, Vermont 05254, 1·802·362·3300.

Our thanks to The Orvis Company, Inc. for the use of a selection of their flies and equipment, and for the information and illustrations contained herein from the Orvis Knot Booklet. For information contact: The Orvis Company, Inc., Historic Route 7A, Manchester, Vermont 05254, 1·800·548·9548.

For their assistance in establishing contacts with charter boat captains, lodging, etc., we thank the Vermont Travel and Tourism Board; the California Division of Trade and Tourism, the Los Angeles Convention and Visitors Bureau, and the San Francisco Convention and Visitors Bureau; the South Carolina Department of Travel and Tourism and the Hilton Head Island Chamber of Commerce. For lodging and logistic assistance during the research portion of this project, we thank the King George Hotel in San Francisco, Calif., the Ritz Carlton Hotel of Marina del Rey, Calif., the Marina del Rey Marriott, Marina del Rey, Calif., the Brittany Inn of Manchester, Vt.; and Kim Petti from Fin & Feather, East Greenwich, R.I.. For sharing their expertise on the water, thanks to Captain Kevin Behan of Maui, Hi., The Hammerhead out of Shelter Cove, Hilton Head Island, S.C., and Captain Gus of Island Water Sports in Hilton Head Island, S.C.

Many thanks to our agent Jennifer Lyons and to our editor Dorothy Williams of Bulfinch Press. I am also grateful to Bill Pekala and the wonderful staff at Nikon Professional Services, for their great cameras, technical assistance and support. For her work in the studio, many thanks to stylist Marcia E. Barrs; for their help in the lab, Norm and Chris at Westwood Photo Productions; and, finally, special thanks for his technical expertise in the darkroom and in the photo studio, go to my old friend and mentor, photographer Richard McCaffrey.